This book belongs to

....

Wet Feet and Other Stories

How this collection works

This *Biff, Chip and Kipper* collection is one of a series of four books at **Read with Oxford Stage 2**. It is divided into two distinct halves.

The first half focuses on phonics, with two stories written in line with the phonics your child will have learned at school: *Shops* and *Wet Feet*. The second half contains two stories that use everyday language: *I Can Trick a Tiger* and *Dragon Danger*. These stories help to broaden your child's wider reading experience. There are also fun activities to enjoy throughout the book.

How to use this book

Find a time to read with your child when they are not too tired and are happy to concentrate for about ten to fifteen minutes. Reading at this stage should be a shared and enjoyable experience. It is best to choose just one story for each session.

There are tips for each part of the book to help you make the most of the stories and activities. The tips for reading on pages 6 and 28 show you how to introduce your child to the phonics stories.

The tips for reading on pages 50 and 72 explain how you can best approach reading the stories that use a wider vocabulary. At the end of each of the four stories you will find four 'Talk about the story' questions. These will help your child to think about what they have read, and to relate the story to their own experiences. The questions are followed by a fun activity.

Enjoy sharing the stories!

Authors and illustrators

Shops written by Roderick Hunt, illustrated by Alex Brychta
Wet Feet written by Roderick Hunt, illustrated by Alex Brychta
I Can Trick a Tiger written by Cynthia Rider, illustrated by Alex Brychta
Dragon Danger written by Cynthia Rider, illustrated by Alex Brychta

OXFORD
UNIVERSITY PRESS

Great Clarendon Street, Oxford, OX2 6DP, United Kingdom

Oxford University Press is a department of the University
of Oxford. It furthers the University's objective of excellence
in research, scholarship, and education by publishing
worldwide. Oxford is a registered trade mark of Oxford
University Press in the UK and in certain other countries

Dragon Danger first published in 2006
Shops, Wet Feet, I Can Trick a Tiger first published in 2007

This Edition published in 2018

British Library Cataloguing in Publication Data
Data available

ISBN: 978-0-19-276419-5

Pack ISBN: 978-0-19-277973-1

10 9 8 7 6 5 4 3 2 1

Paper used in the production of this book is a natural, recyclable product
made from wood grown in sustainable forests. The manufacturing process
conforms to the environmental regulations of the country of origin.

Printed in China by Leo Paper Products Ltd

Acknowledgements

Series Editors: Annemarie Young and Kate Ruttle

Contents

Phonics

Stories for Wider Reading

OXFORD
UNIVERSITY PRESS

Phonics

Children learn best when reading is relaxed and enjoyable.

- Talk about the title and the picture on page 7, and read the speech bubble at the bottom of that page.
- Identify the letter pattern *sh* in the title and talk about the sound it makes when you read it.
- Look at the *sh* words on page 8. Say the sounds in each word and then say the word (e.g. *sh-e-d, shed*).
- Read the story together, then find the words beginning with *sh*.
- Talk about the story and do the fun activity on page 26.

Children enjoy re-reading stories and this helps to build their confidence.

Have fun!

After you have read the story, find five grasshoppers hidden in the pictures.

The main sound practised in this story is 'sh' as in shop.
Other sounds practised are 'i', 'o' and 'a' as in ship, shop and hat.

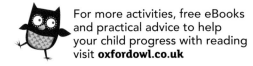

For more activities, free eBooks and practical advice to help your child progress with reading visit **oxfordowl.co.uk**

Shops

What will Kipper buy?

Say the sounds and read the words

shop

ship

shell

shed

shut

shall

Sam had a shop.

"I sell shells," she said.

Pam had a shop.

"This is a ship shop,"
she said.

Pat had a hat shop.

"I sell hats," she said.

"Then I will get a hat,"
said Kipper.

"Shall I get that big hat ...

... this cap ...

... that red hat ...

... this top hat?"

"This shop is shut,"
said Tom.

"This is a pan shop,"
said Tim.

"I sell pans," he said.

"I will get that pan,"
said Kipper.

"This shed is a shop,"
said Chip.

"It is a bun shop," said Biff.

"Buns," said Kipper.

Talk about the story

What did Sam sell in her shop?

Who had the ship shop?

Which shop would you like to visit?

What would you like to sell in a shop?

What's in the picture?

What can you find in the picture that
begins with sh, p, d, b, g, h?

Tips for reading *Wet Feet*

Children learn best when reading is relaxed and enjoyable.

- Talk about the title and the picture on page 29, and read the speech bubble at the bottom of that page.

- Identify the letter pattern *ee* in the title and talk about the sound it makes when you read it.

- Look at the *ee* words on page 30. Say the sounds in each word and then say the word (e.g. *f-ee-t, feet*).

- Read the story together, then find the words with *ee* in them.

- Talk about the story and do the fun activity on page 48.

Children enjoy re-reading stories and this helps to build their confidence.

Have fun!

After you have read the story, find the eight flying birds in the pictures.

The main sound practised in this story is 'ee' as in *deep*.

For more activities, free eBooks and practical advice to help your child progress with reading visit **oxfordowl.co.uk**

Wet Feet

Wilf and Dad go fishing.

Say the sounds and read these words.

deep   feed

feel   need

reel   weed

feet   eel

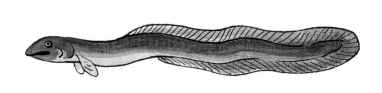

Wilf had a rod and a net.

Wilf and Dad got to the river.

"We can fish in that bit,"
said Dad.

"Let's get fishing," said Wilf.

"Let's feed the fish," said Dad.

"I can feel a fish," said Wilf.

"Reel it in, then," said Dad.

It was not a fish. It was lots
of weeds.

"I can feel a fish," said Dad.

Dad got his feet wet.

Wilf got his feet wet.

"Get the net," said Dad.

It was an eel.

Dad let the eel go.

"We got an eel and wet feet,"
said Wilf. "But no fish."

Talk about the story

Where did Wilf and Dad go fishing?

What did they catch?

How did they get wet feet?

What do you like doing at the weekend?

Jumbled letters

Make the *ee* words.

Stories for Wider Reading

Tips for reading the stories together

These two stories use simple everyday language. You can help your child to read any more challenging words in the context of the story. Children enjoy re-reading stories and this helps to build their confidence and their vocabulary.

Tips for reading *I Can Trick a Tiger*

- Talk about the title and the speech bubble on page 51, and look through the pictures so that your child can see what the story is about.
- Read the story together, encouraging your child to read as much as they can with you.
- Give lots of praise as your child reads with you, and help them when necessary.
- If your child gets stuck on a word that is easily decodable, encourage them to say the sounds and then blend them together to read the word. Read the whole sentence again. Focus on the meaning. If the word is not decodable, or is still too tricky, just read the word for them and move on.
- When you've finished reading the story, talk about it with your child, using the 'Talk about the story' questions at the end.
- Do the activity on page 70.
- Re-read the story later, again encouraging your child to read as much of it as they can.

Have fun!

After you have read *I Can Trick a Tiger*, find the tree frog hidden in every picture.

This book includes these useful common words:

look   said   you   out

For more activities, free eBooks and practical advice to help your child progress with reading visit **oxfordowl.co.uk**

I Can Trick a Tiger

Can Floppy trick a tiger?

Floppy was dreaming.
He was in the jungle.

A tiger jumped out.
"Got you!" he said.

"I can trick a tiger,"
said Floppy.

"Look out!" said Floppy.
"There is a bee on your nose."

"Oh no!" said the tiger,
and he let Floppy go.

A crocodile jumped out.
"Got you!" she said.

"I can trick a crocodile,"
said Floppy.

"Look out!" said Floppy.
"There is a bee on your nose."

"Oh no!" said the crocodile,
and she let Floppy go.

A snake slid out.
"Got you!" she said.

"I can trick a snake,"
said Floppy.

"Look out!" said Floppy.
"There is a bee on your nose."

"Oh no!" said the snake,
and she let Floppy go.

A rabbit jumped out.
"Got you!" said Floppy.

"Look out!" said the rabbit.
"There is a bee on your nose."

Buzzzzzzzzz!

"Oh no!" said Floppy.

Talk about the story

Why did
the tiger let
Floppy go?

What would you
do if you had a bee
on your nose?

How do you think
Floppy felt when the bee
landed on his nose?

Have you ever
played a trick on
anybody? Was it a
funny trick?

Rhyming words

Match the things that rhyme.

Tips for reading *Dragon Danger*

- Talk about the title and the speech bubble on page 73, and look through the pictures so that your child can see what the story is about.

- Read the story together, encouraging your child to read as much as they can with you.

- Give lots of praise as your child reads with you, and help them when necessary.

- If your child gets stuck on a word that is easily decodable, encourage them to say the sounds and then blend them together to read the word. Read the whole sentence again. Focus on the meaning. If the word is not decodable, or is still too tricky, just read the word for them and move on.

- When you've finished reading the story, talk about it with your child, using the 'Talk about the story' questions at the end.

- Do the activity on page 92.

- Re-read the story later, again encouraging your child to read as much of it as they can.

Have fun!

After you have read *Dragon Danger*, find the 10 different reptiles hidden in the pictures

This book includes these useful common words:

saw   said   came   out   she

For more activities, free eBooks and practical advice to help your child progress with reading visit **oxfordowl.co.uk**

Dragon Danger

Is Floppy in danger?

Floppy was dreaming about
dragons.

Floppy saw a baby dragon
with its mother.

The mother dragon saw Floppy.
"Go away," she roared.

The dragon roared again and
flapped her wings.

She flew at Floppy.
"Oh help!" he said.

WHOOSH! Flames came
out of the dragon's mouth.

Floppy hid, but the
dragon saw him.

Floppy ran onto a bridge.
WHOOSH! Flames came out
of the dragon's mouth again.

"Help!" said Floppy.
"The bridge is on fire."

Floppy ran back across
the bridge.

He ran past a rock and saw
the baby dragon again.

The mother dragon roared
at Floppy. She flew up
onto a high rock.

Oh no! The rock started to fall.

CRASH!

The rock fell down ...

... but Floppy pulled the baby dragon out of danger.

"Phew! Just in time," he said.

What a brave dog!

Talk about the story

Why did the mother dragon roar at Floppy?

Why couldn'l Floppy hide from the dragon?

How do you think Floppy felt when the rock started to fall?

What other dragon stories do you know?

A maze

Help Floppy find his way out of the dragon's maze.

Remembering the stories together

Encourage your child to remember and retell the stories in this book. You could ask questions like these:

- Who are the characters in the story?

- What happens at the beginning of the story?

- What happens next?

- How does the story end?

- What was your favourite part of the story? Why?

Story prompts

When talking to your child about the stories, you could use these more detailed reminders to help them remember the exact sequence of events. Turn the statements below into questions, so that your child can give you the answers. For example, *What are the children playing? What is Pam selling?* And so on …

Shops

- The children are playing shops. Sam has a shop and she sells shells.

- Pam has a shop and she sells ships.

- Pat has a shop and she sells hats.

- Kipper gets a hat.

- He gets a pan from Tim's shop.

- He gets a bun at the shed.

Wet Feet

- Wilf and his dad go fishing in the river.

- Dad feeds the fish to bring them closer.

- Dad teaches Wilf to fish, but Wilf catches weeds instead of fish!

- They both get in the river.

- They catch an eel instead of a fish.

- Then Dad lets the eel go.

I Can Trick a Tiger

- Floppy dreams that he's in the jungle.

- A tiger jumps out, but Floppy manages to trick him.

- A crocodile jumps out, but Floppy manages to trick her, too.

- Then a snake slides out, but Floppy manages to trick her, too.

- Floppy tries to catch a rabbit, but the rabbit uses Floppy's trick to get away.

Dragon Danger

- Floppy is dreaming about seeing a mother and baby dragon.

- The mother dragon tells Floppy to go away and leave her baby dragon alone.

- The mother dragon breathes fire to scare Floppy, but the bridge catches fire.

- Floppy is worried when he sees the rock wobbling above the baby dragon.

- Then the rock falls.

- Floppy saves the baby dragon!

You could now encourage your child to create a 'story map' of each story, drawing and colouring all the key parts of them. This will help them to identify the main elements of the stories and learn to create their own stories.